MAGIC IN MY WORDS

Written by

Ariyana & Ariyelle Cofield

Illustrated by

Anastasia Cartovenco

MAGIC IN MY WORDS

Copyright © 2021 by Ari Magia Publishing

Written by Ariyana & Ariyelle Cofield

All rights reserved. No part of this book may be used or reproduced in any manner whatsoever without prior written permission from the publisher.

Paperback: 978-1-7377048-1-2

Hardcover: 978-1-7377048-2-9

Dedication

We thank God for the opportunity to write this book and would like to dedicate it to all boys and girls. Always love yourself, know that you are amazing just the way you are and remember that there is magic inside of you!

THIS BOOK BELONGS TO:

____

I have magic because I am
SMART.

I am smart and have big dreams.

I never give up and I learn new things.

I have magic because I am
KIND.

I am always a good friend
and help people in need.

I show kindness to others
and they show it back to me.

I have magic because I am
SPECIAL.

I know no one acts or looks like me.
That makes me special as I can be.

I have magic because I am
IMPORTANT.

There is nothing around worth more than me.
I am important for the world to see.

I have magic because I am
LOVED.

I do what I love every day and night.
I love myself and I do what is right.

I have magic because I am
THANKFUL.

Thankful for family and my friends too.
Thankful for all things that are good and true.

I have magic because I am
AMAZING.

I am amazing can't you see?
It is wonderful just being me.

I have magic because I am a WINNER.

I am a winner because I don't stop.
I dream it, I do it, and I make it to the top.

I have magic because I am
HAPPY.

Happiness is inside of me.
My smile is my symbol for all to see.

I have magic because I am
POWERFUL.